Kama Sutra

ISBN: 81-7437-015-3

Reprinted 1997

First published by
Lustre Press Pvt. Ltd.
M-75, GK II Market
New Delhi - 110 002, INDIA
Phones: (011) 6442271, 6462782
Fax: (011) 6467185

*Man is divided into three classes: the
hare man, the bull man and the horse
man according to the size of his lingam.
Woman also, according to the depth of
her yoni, is either a female deer, a mare
or a female elephant.*

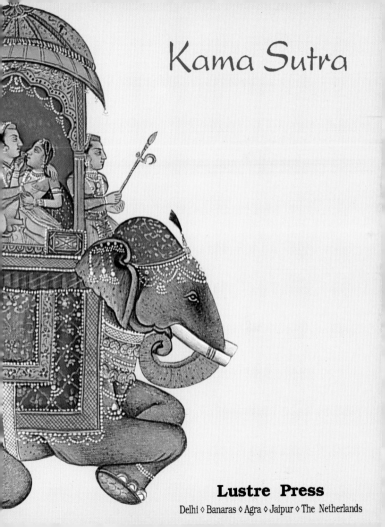

Kama Sutra

Lustre Press

Delhi ◊ Banaras ◊ Agra ◊ Jaipur ◊ The Netherlands

TRANSLATED as the 'Art of Love' or 'Aphorisms on Love' Vatsyayana's *Kama Sutra* is famous the world over as a classic on love and love-making. Written sometime between the first and fourth centuries A.D. by the sage Vatsyayana as a part of his scholarly exercises at Banaras, the *Kama Sutra* is less a treatise on sex than a treatise on conduct. It embodies an attitude to life that gets rarer by the day—an attitude that teaches us that the world is eminently enjoyable and love and sex even more so; that men and women have an equal right to pleasure and should search for ways and means of enhancing it. The *Kama Sutra* instructs us not only in the art of love and sex but also in the value of singing, dancing, conversation, dressing and living well.

The picture that Vatsyayana paints of his life and times is fascinating. Here are some excerpts, to give you the flavour of the original, little asides that many people miss in their chase of 'the sixty-four' postures of

Facing page: One of the signs of a woman manifesting love is when she shows herself to her lover in secret places.

Overleaf spread: When a woman lifts her thighs and the man lies across, riding upon her buttocks, it is called the 'conch'.

love. Vatsyayana defines an ideal dwelling place as one which is situated near water surrounded by a garden, contains rooms, balmy with rich perfumes, with a soft bed, low in the middle part, having garlands and bunches of flowers upon it, a canopy above it and two pillows, one at the top and one at the bottom. There should be a sort of stool on which fragrant ointments for the night, pots containing collyrium and other fragrant substances and things used for perfuming the mouth should be kept.

The householder, having got up in the morning

When one of two lovers presses forcibly one or both of the thighs of the other between his or her own it is called the 'embrace of thighs'.

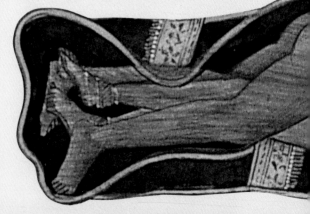

should wash his teeth, apply a limited quantity of ointments and perfumes to his body, put some ornaments on his person, colour his lips and look at himself in the glass. He should bathe daily, anoint his body with oil every other day, and get his head (including face) shaved every four days while other parts of his body every five or ten days. All these things should be done without fail and the sweat of the armpits should also be removed. . . . In the evening there should be singing   and after that the

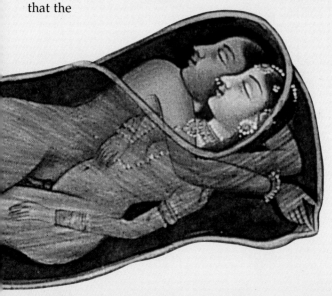

householder, along with his friend should await in his room, the arrival of the woman. After her arrival, he and his friend should entertain her with a loving conversation. Thus end the duties of the day.

A female should learn the *Kama Sutra*, by studying its practice from some confidential friend. She should study alone in private the sixty-four practices that form

The women of the royal harem cannot see or meet any men on account of their being strictly guarded; neither do they have their desires satisfied because their husband is common to many wives. For this reason among themselves they give pleasure to each other in various ways.

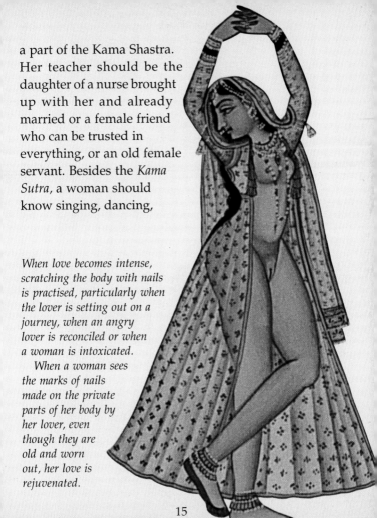

a part of the Kama Shastra. Her teacher should be the daughter of a nurse brought up with her and already married or a female friend who can be trusted in everything, or an old female servant. Besides the *Kama Sutra*, a woman should know singing, dancing,

When love becomes intense, scratching the body with nails is practised, particularly when the lover is setting out on a journey, when an angry lover is reconciled or when a woman is intoxicated.

When a woman sees the marks of nails made on the private parts of her body by her lover, even though they are old and worn out, her love is rejuvenated.

playing on musical instruments, writing and drawing, trimming and decoration, magic or sorcery, quickness of hand, culinary art, mimicry or imitation, carpentry, knowledge about gold and silver, gardening, teaching parrots to speak, composing poems, gambling and a host of other arts.

The following are the places for kissing, namely, the forehead, the eyes, the cheeks, the throat, the bosom, the breasts, the nipples, the lips and the interior of the mouth. On the occasion of the first congress, kissing, embracing and pressing or scratching with nails or fingers should be done moderately.

When a man begs to be allowed to have sexual intercourse with a woman, she should let him touch her private parts only. The man should then loosen her girdle and the knot of her dress and turning her lower garment, should shampoo gently the joints of her naked thighs.

When the legs are contracted and thus held by the lover before his bosom, it is called the 'pressed position'. When both the legs of the woman are contracted and placed on her stomach, it is called the 'crab's position'.

Previous spread: When a man presses the jaghana or the middle part of the woman's body against his own and mounts upon her to practice, it is called the 'embrace of the jaghana'.

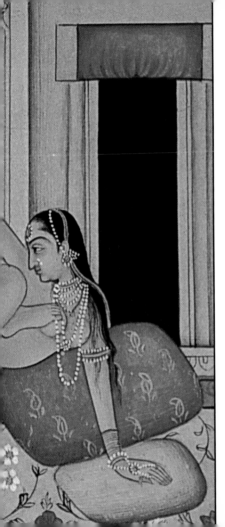

That part of the Kama Sutra which treats of sexual union is called the 'sixty-four' and contains eight subjects: the embrace, kissing, scratching with the nails or fingers, biting, lying down, making various sounds, playing the part of a man and the mouth congress or auparishtaka. Each of these subjects being of eight kinds and eight multiplied by eight being sixty-four, this part is, therefore, aptly named sixty-four. However, some of Vatsyayana's sixty-four positions seem to be meant specially for acrobats and contortionists.

When, while engaged in congress, a woman turns round like a wheel, it is called the 'top'. This is learnt by practice only.

When a curved mark is made on the breast by means of the five nails, it is called a 'peacock's foot'.

An ingenious person should try out different kinds of congress by imitating the manner of the different kinds of beasts and birds. In this way can be carried on the congress of the Hastika or elephant and the Mrigi or deer.

When the man lifts up the middle part of his body and the woman turns round her middle part, it is called the 'swing'.

And if men and woman learn to swing to each other's rhythm, their love will not be lessened even in one hundred years.

When a man and woman support themselves on each other's bodies while standing in a congress, it is called the 'tripod' or 'supported congress'.

When a woman lowers her head and raises her middle part, it is called the 'widely opened position'.

On the occassion of a 'high congress', the Mrigi (deer) woman should lie down in such a way as to widen her yoni, while in a 'low congress' the Hastini (elephant) woman should lie down so as he contract hers. But in an 'equal congress' they should lie down in a natural position. What is said concerning the Mrigi and Hastini applies also to the Vadawa or mare. In a 'low congress' a woman should particularly make use of medicine, to cause her desires to be satisfied quickly.

Previous spread: When his lingam is erect, a man should touch her with his hands in various places and gently manipulate various parts of her body. If the woman is bashful the man should place his hands between her thighs. . . . If, however, she is a seasoned woman he should do whatever is agreeable to him or to her.

When she raises her thighs and keeps them wide apart and engages in congress, it is called the 'yawning position'.

When during congress she turns around and gets on top of her lover in such a manner as to continue the congress without obstructing the pleasure of it then the woman is said to be doing the work of a man.

Following spread: When a woman sees that her lover is fatigued by constant congress, without having his desire satisfied, she should, with his permission, lay him down upon his back and give him assistance by acting his part.

When a man enjoys two women at the same time both of whom love him equally, it is called the 'united congress'.

When a man, though having congress with one woman thinks all
the time that he is enjoying another one whom he loves, it is called
the congress of 'transferred love'.

When the organs are brought together properly and directly it is called 'moving the organ forward'. When the yoni is lowered and the upper part of it is struck with the lingam it is called 'piercing'.

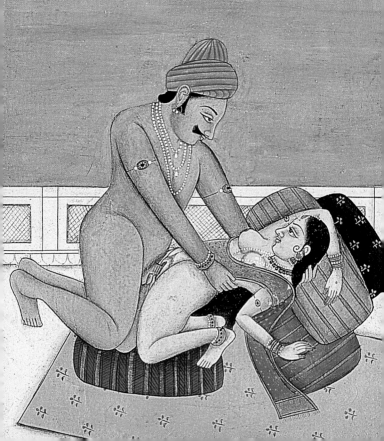

When the lingam is in the yoni and is moved up and down
frequently without being withdrawn, it is called the 'sporting of a
sparrow'.

When a man embraces his lover in his arms, and parts her knees,
sinking into her thereby crushing her, it is called 'churning curd'.

When only one part of the yoni is rubbed with the lingam, it is called the 'blow of a boar'. When both sides of the yoni are rubbed in this way, it is called the 'blow of a bull'.

The heightening of pleasure in men and women arouses different awareness. While the man feels 'this woman is united with me', the woman thinks 'I am united with this man'.

When a woman forcibly holds in her yoni the lingam after it is in, it is called the 'hare's position'. This is learnt by practice only.

When a man enjoys many women at the same time, it is called the 'congress of a herd of cows'.

Many young men may enjoy one woman, who may be married to one of them, either one after the other or at the same time. Thus, one of them holds her, another enjoys her, a third uses her mouth, a fourth holds her middle part and in this way they go on enjoying her several parts alternately.

When a man and a woman embrace each other as if they were entering into each other's bodies either while the woman is sitting on the lap of the man, or in front of him, or on a bed, then it is called an embrace like 'a mixture of milk and water'.

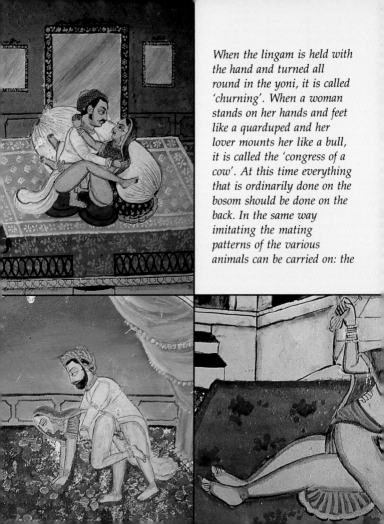

When the lingam is held with the hand and turned all round in the yoni, it is called 'churning'. When a woman stands on her hands and feet like a quarduped and her lover mounts her like a bull, it is called the 'congress of a cow'. At this time everything that is ordinarily done on the bosom should be done on the back. In the same way imitating the mating patterns of the various animals can be carried on: the congress of a dog, the congress of a goat, the congress of a deer, the forcible mounting of an ass, the congress of a cat, the jump of a tiger, the pressing of an elephant, the rubbing of a boar and the mounting of a horse.

There are also nine kinds of union depending upon the size of the man's organ and the woman's yoni, and the force of passion or carnal desires.

To aim well and shoot
has always been
good advice.

A horse having once attained the fifth degree of motion goes on with blind speed; in the same manner a loving pair becomes blind with passion in the heat of congress and go on with great impetuosity, paying not the least regard to excess.